International Passport Series

The Great Irish Songbook

Arranged and Edited by Dan Fox

With a special section of traditional Irish jigs, reels and hornpipes

CARL FISCHER®
62 Cooper Square, New York, NY 10003

ATF118

ISBN 0-8258-1014-0

Contents

284
9RE

Believe Me If All Those Endearing Young Charms 16

Cockles and Mussels — see *Molly Malone* 30

Colleen Dhas Cruthen Na Moe — see *The Pretty Girl Milking Her Cow* 32

Come Back to Erin 48

Danny Boy 50

Devil's Dream 123

Drill, Ye Tarriers, Drill! 52

Foggy Dew, The 18

Garryowen 124

Girl I Left Behind Me, The 20

Green Little Shamrock, The (or, The Dear Little Shamrock) 54

Harp That Once Through Tara's Halls, The 22

Harrigan 79

Has Anybody Here Seen Kelly? 73

I'll Take You Home Again, Kathleen 56

Ireland Must Be Heaven (For My Mother Came from There) 68

Irish Emmigrant, The 24

Irish Washerwoman, The 125

Irish Wedding Song, The (or, The Wedding Song) 12

It's a Long, Long Way to Tipperary 70

I've Got Rings on My Fingers (or, Mumbo Jumbo Jijjiboo J. O'Shea) 76

Kathleen Mavourneen 40

Kerry Dance, The 26

Killarney 58

Little Annie Rooney 88

Little Bit of Heaven, A (Shure They Call It Ireland) 85

Macushla 82

Contents continued

Mary's a Grand Old Name 92

McNamara's Band 94

Minstrel Boy, The 43

Molly Bawn 28

Molly Malone (Cockles and Mussels) 30

Mother Machree 98

Mumbo Jumbo Jijjiboo J. O'Shea — see *I've Got Rings on My Fingers* 76

My Wild Irish Rose 100

Paddy Whack 126

Paddy Works on the Railway 60

Peg O' My Heart 109

Pretty Girl Milking Her Cow, The (Colleen Dhas Cruthen Na Moe) 32

Rory O'More 34

Rose of Tralee, The 36

St. Patrick's Day in the Morning 127

Shure They Call It Ireland — see *A Little Bit of Heaven* 85

Stack O' Barley 128

Sweet Rosie O'Grady 103

That Tumble-down Shack in Athlone 64

That's an Irish Lullaby — see *Too-ra-loo-ra-loo-ral* 106

'Tis the Last Rose of Summer 38

Too-ra-loo-ra-loo-ral (That's an Irish Lullaby) 106

Wearing of the Green, The 45

Wedding Song, The — see *The Irish Wedding Song* 12

When Irish Eyes Are Smiling 119

Where the River Shannon Flows 62

Who Threw The Overalls in Mistress Murphy's Chowder? 116

You Can Tell That I'm Irish 112

Foreword

The origins of the music of Ireland, like the origins of the Celts who originally settled there, are shrouded in mystery. What is certain is that from the earliest times, music played an important role in Irish culture. Consider these words written by John of Salisbury in the 12th century:

"The attention of [the Irish] to musical instruments I find worthy of commendation, in which their skill is beyond comparison superior to that of any nation I have seen."

The earliest instruments in Irish music were the harp and the bagpipe, which were then augmented with flutes (pennywhistles) and violins. In later times the banjo was imported from America and took its place as an important instrument of the Irish ensemble. The accordion, too, emigrated to Ireland in the mid-19th century and remains popular there today. The peculiar Irish drum known as the bodhran also plays an important role.

The earliest Irish music of which we have examples is found in the early 17th century "Fitzwilliam Virginal Book" which is still in print after nearly 400 years. In the early 19th century, Thomas Moore (1779-1852) published his first book of lyrics set to traditional Irish melodies. This treasure included many songs still in the semi-classical repertoire including "Believe Me if All Those Endearing Young Charms," "The Harp That Once Through Tara's Halls," "The Minstrel Boy," and "'Tis the Last Rose of Summer," all found in this book.

Although there had always been many Irish emigrating to America, the terrible famine of 1839-40 caused a tremendous flood of impoverished people to flee to the relative affluence and freedom of the United States. Their lot here was hard, and many songs reflect this difficult period ("Paddy Works on the Railway," "Drill, Ye Tarriers, Drill!"). And, of course, as miserable as conditions had been in the old country, the Irish felt homesick and expressed their longing in beautiful songs such as "Come Back to Erin," "That Tumble-down Shack in Athlone," and many others.

At first a despised minority ("No Irish need apply"),the Irish soon became active in various occupations, especially politics and law enforcement, in which their natural conviviality was to their great advantage. Within one or two generations they became the darlings of vaudeville and later the

Lynchs Castle, Galway

legitimate stage. George M. Cohan (1878-1942) was the best known of these Irish-American stars, but he was by no means the only one. Maggie Cline, C.W. Murphy, James Molloy, Michael Nolan, Ernest R. Ball, Chauncey Olcott, Alfred Bryan, and others lit up the American stage for many years. Irish musicals were an important part of Broadway until well after World War I, and many of those songs are still sung including "Too-ra-loo-ra-loo-ral (That's an Irish Lullaby)," "My Wild Irish Rose," and "When Irish Eyes Are Smiling."

The Irish have always loved dancing as well as music, and included in this book is a section of traditional reels, jigs, and hornpipes, including "The Irish Washerwoman," "Garryowen," "Stack O'Barley," and others, which are still played by Irish bands both in America and on the "ould sod."

And on a final note, no book would be really complete without Ian Betteridge's modern classic "Irish Wedding Song," which has captured the tender spirit of the festive occasion of marriage.

We, the publishers, feel that this collection of Irish music of the last 200 years is the most complete and musically satisfying songbook of its type ever published. Dan Fox, one of America's best-loved arrangers, has simplified the songs to put them within the reach of any moderately skilled player, without sacrificing any of the melodic beauty so characteristic of this, some of the world's loveliest music.

The Songs of Old Ireland

Believe Me If All Those Endearing Young Charms 16
Foggy Dew, The 18
Girl I Left Behind Me, The 20
Harp That Once Through Tara's Halls, The 22
Irish Emigrant, The 24
Kathleen Mavourneen 40
Kerry Dance, The 26

Minstrel Boy, The 43
Molly Bawn 28
Molly Malone (Cockles and Mussels) 30
Pretty Girl Milking Her Cow, The 32
Rory O'More 34
Rose of Tralee, The 36
'Tis the Last Rose of Summer 38

The Irish Come to America

Come Back to Erin 48
Danny Boy 50
Drill, Ye Tarriers, Drill! 52
Green Little Shamrock, The
    (or, The Dear Little Shamrock) 54
I'll Take You Home Again, Kathleen 52

Killarney 58
Paddy Works on the Railway 60
That Tumble-Down Shack in Athlone 64
Wearing of the Green, The 45
Where the River Shannon Flows 62

The Irish on Stage

Harrigan 79
Has Anybody Here Seen Kelly? 73
Ireland Must Be Heaven
    (For My Mother Came From There) 68
It's A Long, Long Way to Tipperary 70
I've Got Rings on My Fingers 76
Little Annie Rooney 88
Little Bit of Heaven, A (Shure They Call It Ireland) 85
Macushla 82
Mary's A Grand Old Name 92

McNamara's Band 94
Mother Machree 98
My Wild Irish Rose 100
Peg O' My Heart 109
Sweet Rosie O'Grady 103
Too-ra-loo-ra-loo-ral (That's an Irish Lullaby) 106
When Irish Eyes Are Smiling 119
Who Threw the Overalls in Mistress
    Murphy's Chowder? 116
You Can Tell That I'm Irish 112

Jigs, Reels and Hornpipes

Devil's Dream 123
Garryowen 124
Irish Washerwoman, The 125

Paddy Whack 126
St. Patrick's Day in the Morning 127
Stack o' Barley 128

And . . .

Irish Wedding Song, The 12

About the Songs

The Music of Old Ireland

Undoubtedly the most important figure in 19th century Irish music was Thomas Moore. Born in Dublin in 1779, he was a self-taught pianist and singer who became a popular entertainer in the houses of the aristocracy. In 1807 he published the first of a series of lyrics set to traditional Irish melodies. Although he was criticized for altering the modal characteristics of the tunes, the four songs in this section, "Believe Me If All Those Endearing Young Charms," "The Harp That Once Through Tara's Halls," (Tara was the ancient residence of Irish kings) "The Minstrel Boy," and the exquisite "'Tis the Last Rose of Summer," have had a lasting impact on the world's song repertoire. The origins of some of the other songs in this section are more obscure. "Molly Malone," also known as "Cockles and Mussels," is supposedly based on actual street cries of 18th century Dublin. "The Pretty Girl Milking Her Cow" started out as the Gaelic song "Colleen dhas cruthen na moe" in 9/8 time and in the Dorian mode. The arranger Alexander Lee is given credit for translating the words into English and (less commendably) "modernizing" the scale and meter. Another traditional song is "The Girl I Left Behind Me." The earliest printed version dates from 1810, almost 35 years after the events of 1776 with which the tune is often associated. James Molloy (1837-1909), who would later achieve fame as the writer of "Love's Old Sweet Song," was an Irishman who based his "Kerry Dance" on an earlier composition called "The Cuckoo" (1790). Molloy wrote new words and a middle section to give us the song we know today. Samuel Lover was a multi-talented Irish novelist, poet, painter and composer who lived from 1797 to 1868. He wrote many songs including "Rory O'More" and "Molly Bawn" which appear in this book. The latter song was interpolated into a comic opera called "Il Paddy Whack in Italia," a spoof of Italian opera. Lover was the grandfather of one of America's finest popular composers, Victor Herbert. "The Rose of Tralee," surely one of the loveliest melodies ever written, was composed by Irishman John William Glover (1815-1899). He was the editor of an 1850's edition of Thomas Moore's "Irish Melodies" and also wrote many original works for piano and chorus as well as an opera,"The Deserted Village," and a cantata, "St. Patrick at Tara."

Westport House, County Mayo

The Irish Come to America

Although many Irish had come to America during the Colonial period and the half century following the Revolution, the terrible potato famine of 1839-40 caused more than a million impoverished peasants to flood into America. At first the Americans were appalled at the sheer numbers of unkempt and often illiterate people, and posters that read "No Irish need apply" were all too common where work might be found. But the Irish had two things going for them. First, of course, was the fact that they spoke English, giving them an edge over the Swedes, Germans, and other nationalities. Second, the Irish are a naturally likeable people. The typical Irishman, although difficult when he gets angry, is a charming, gregarious sort of person who makes friends easily and loves to share his good feelings with others. This made the Irish naturals for American politics. Within one generation they became an important force in city, state, and even national politics, an importance they hold to this day (Think of the Kennedys, for example!).

Two early songs illustrate the lot of the Irish blue-collar worker. "Paddy Works on the Railway" details the importance of the Irish in the spread of the railroad in America.

"Drill, Ye Tarriers, Drill!" is an ironic commentary on the condition of the Irish "pick and shovel" man. ("Tarrier" was a slang word referring to excavation workers.) The Irish also had a great deal of affection for the "ould sod," and this is reflected in many songs. "Come Back to Erin," although written by an Englishwoman under the pseudonym "Claribel," was a great favorite, as was "The Green Little Shamrock," "Killarney," "That Tumble-down Shack in Athlone," and "Where the River Shannon Flows." These sentimental ballads brought a tear to many an Irish eye, especially those who had not experienced firsthand the poverty and degradation of life in the old country under British rule. Even "I'll Take You Home Again, Kathleen" became an Irish favorite, although written by an American of German descent who never mentions where Kathleen's home

is. But undoubtedly the most popular nostalgic song of Ireland is "Danny Boy." This ancient Irish melody, called "Londonderry Air," has been called the most beautiful ever written. Many lyricists had tried setting words to it, including the great Thomas Moore who called his version "Would God I Were the Tender Apple Blossom." Ironically, it took an Englishman, Fred Weatherly, to give us the version known and loved throughout the English-speaking world. His "Danny Boy" dates from 1913. The political situation in the old country was never far from the mind of Dion Boucicault, an Irish-born American playwright whose 1865 play "Arrah Na Pogue" featured a spirited performance of the song "The Wearing of the Green." Boucicault set his bitter lyric to an anonymous melody that dates back to the 18th century.

Inishmore, Aran Islands

The Irish on Stage

Along with politics, the Irish soon made their mark in entertainment. Every performer knows that being liked is the first step in a successful career, and being liked is something that every Irishman and woman knows how to do. In 1889 Michael Nolan had a tremendous hit with "Little Annie Rooney." Nolan was an Irish entertainer working in the English music halls, and Annie was his three year old cousin. How the song got to America is anybody's guess, but it was the biggest hit of its time. "Sweet Rosie O'Grady" was the work of vaudevillian Maude Nugent, whose performances of the song made it a hit in 1896. There are still many sing-along bars named in honor of Ms. O'Grady in New York, Orlando, and other cities. A great hit of 1898 was the hilarious "Who Threw the Overalls in Mistress Murphy's Chowder?" The Irish have never been afraid to make fun of themselves, and this song is as fresh and funny today as the day it was written. "Has Anybody Here Seen Kelly?" was originally an English music hall song about an Irishman who takes his girl friend on a day trip to the Isle of Man but disappears during the day's festivities. Wm. J. McKenna adapted the words for American audiences with great success. In 1909 Blanche Ring, a vaudeville star of the day, made a hit out of "I've Got Rings on My Fingers," a nonsense song about a likeable Irishman who becomes the ruler of an exotic island near India. "Macushla" was written in 1910, but remained obscure until the great John McCormack made it a part of his repertoire. McCormack, who lived from 1884-1945, was a fantastically popular singer whose pure Irish tenor launched many a song into the realm of standards. Chauncey Olcott first came to the attention of the listening public with "My Wild Irish Rose" in 1899. Olcott became very well known as the composer of American musicals with Irish themes such as "Barry of Ballymore" which featured the tearjerker "Mother Machree." Again, it was John McCormack who turned this song into the standard it remains. Olcott was also a fine performer. His rendition of "Too-ra-loo-ra-loo-ral (That's an Irish Lullaby)," by J.R. Shannon was the high spot of the 1913 show "Shameen Dhu" (Black-haired Jimmy) and remained the definitive interpretation of the song until Bing Crosby sang it in the 1944 film, "Going My Way." Olcott's most famous song is the still often performed "When Irish Eyes Are Smiling" which he wrote with George Graff and Ernest R. Ball in 1912. Perhaps no other song captures the Irish spirit as perfectly as this one. It comes from the play "Isle O' Dreams." Other famous Irish-American songs found in this section are "Ireland Must Be Heaven (For My Mother Came from There)," the 1914 "A Little Bit of Heaven (Shure They Call

Gleanveagh Castle and National Park,
County Donegal

It Ireland)" and the ever-popular "McNamara's Band." "Peg O'My Heart" was named after a Laurette Taylor stage play—not a musical. It had only indifferent success until 1947 when a Harmonicats recording made it into an international hit. "It's a Long, Long Way to Tipperary" was the work of two English vaudevillians, Jack Judge and Harry Williams. Originally intended as a gentle spoof of an Irish bumpkin in London, the song's rousing chorus made it a favorite with the British tommies during World War I.

No discussion of Irish-American music would be complete without the towering figure of George M. Cohan. Cohan was born on July 3, 1878. Later, when Cohan became known as the patriot "born on the fourth of July," his real birthdate became a source of amusement to his many friends in show business. He came from a family of entertainers and was soon on the stage himself as a song and dance man. His charm and talent enabled him to strike out on his own, and his contributions to the American stage included many musicals and innumerable songs including "The Yankee Doodle Boy" (better known as "Yankee Doodle Dandy"), "Give My Regards to Broadway," "You're A Grand Old Flag," and "Over There," the World War I marching song that won him a Congressional Medal. Although proud of his Irish heritage, Cohan wrote only a few specifically Irish songs. The most famous of these is

"Harrigan" from his 1908 musical "Fifty Miles from Boston." The song was a tribute to real life vaudeville entertainer Ned Harrigan of the famous team of Harrigan and Hart. "Mary's a Grand Old Name," though not specifically Irish, has a definite Hibernian lilt to the chorus. Cohan's most sincere tribute to his heritage, although written to be sung by a woman, was "You Can Tell That I'm Irish," from "The Cohan Review of 1916." Cohan was immortalized in the 1942 movie "Yankee Doodle Dandy" which featured an Academy Award performance from James Cagney, whose Irish charm rivaled Cohan's own. Later, the Broadway musical "George M." familiarized a new generation with Cohan's great songs and colorful life.

Jigs, Reels and Hornpipes

Also included in this book is a short section of Irish dance music. The jig usually has two strains of equal length. The reel is similar to the Scottish dance of the same name. The hornpipe was originally a step dance in triple time. Around the time of the American Revolution hornpipes began to be performed in common time. Reels and jigs are usually in 6/8 time with a strong duple feeling. All the tunes in this section are still performed at Irish affairs especially "Garryowen," "The Irish Washerwoman," and "Stack O' Barley" which epitomize the stout hearts and good spirits of the Irish people.

And, speaking of the stout hearts and good spirits of the Irish people, we have included in this book "The Irish Wedding Song" where the words and melody capture the tender spirit of the wedding celebration.

Acknowledgement
Photos: Courtesy of the Irish Tourist Board, 345 Park Ave., New York, NY 10154

Lough Derg, County Donegal

Index of First Lines

Note: The first line or phrase of each song appears in this index. If the song has a verse and chorus, the first line of each is listed.

Alive, alive-o...(Molly Malone) 30

A winning way, a pleasant smile...(Little Annie Rooney) 88

Believe me if all those endearing young charms 16

By Killarney's lakes and fells...(Killarney) 58

Come back to Erin, Mavourneen, Mavourneen 48

Fil-le-me-oo-re-i-re-ay...(Paddy Works on the Railway) 60

For it is Mary, Mary...(Mary's a Grand Old Name) 92

H-A-double R-I-G-A-N spells Harrigan 79

Has anybody here seen Kelly? 73

Have you ever heard the story of how Ireland got its name? (A Little Bit of Heaven) 85

Here they stand, hand in hand...(The Irish Wedding Song) 12

I can sing "Yankee Doodle" as much as I please (You Can Tell That I'm Irish) 112

If you listen I'll sing you a sweet little song...(My Wild Irish Rose) 100

I grow tired of a song if it lingers too long...(Peg O' My Heart) 109

I'll take you home again, Kathleen 56

I'm a long way from home...(That Tumble-down Shack in Athlone) 64

I'm sitting on the stile, Mary...(The Irish Emigrant) 24

In Dublin's fair city...(Molly Malone) 30

In eighteen hundred and forty one...(Paddy Works on the Railway) 60

In good times and bad times...(The Irish Wedding Song) 12

It's a long way to Tipperary...(It's a Long, Long Way to Tipperary) 70

It was on a fine summer's morning...(The Pretty Girl Milking Her Cow) 32

I've often heard my daddy speak...(Ireland Must Be Heaven) 68

Jim O'Shea was cast away...(I've Got Rings on My Fingers) 76

Just around the corner...(Sweet Rosie O'Grady) 103

Kathleen Mavourneen! the grey dawn is breaking 40

Macushla! Macushla! your sweet voice is calling 82

Michael Kelly with his sweetheart came from County Cork...(Has Anybody Here Seen Kelly?) 73

Mistress Murphy gave a party...(Who Threw the Overalls in Mistress Murphy's Chowder?) 116

My mother's name was Mary...(Mary's a Grand Old Name) 92

My Wild Irish Rose, the sweetest flow'r that grows 100

Oh! a wan cloud was drawn o'er the dim weeping dawn...(The Foggy Dew) 18

Index of First Lines

Oh, Danny Boy, the pipes, the pipes are calling...(Danny Boy) 50

Oh, ev'ry morn at sev'n o'clock...(Drill, Ye Tarriers, Drill!) 52

Oh, I want to go back to that tumble-down shack

    (That Tumble-down Shack in Athlone) 64

Oh, me name is McNamara...(McNamara's Band) 94

Oh, Molly Bawn, why leave me pining...(Molly Bawn) 28

Oh, Paddy, dear...(The Wearing of the Green) 45

Oh, the days of the Kerry dancing...(The Kerry Dance) 26

Over in Killarney, many years ago...(Too-ra-loo-ra-loo-ral) 106

Peg O' my heart, I love you 109

She's my sweetheart...(Little Annie Rooney) 88

She's the most distressful country...(The Wearing of the Green) 45

Shure, a little bit of heaven fell from out the sky one day...(A Little Bit of Heaven) 85

Sure, I love the dear silver that shines in your hair...(Mother Machree) 98

Sure, I've got rings on my fingers 76

Sweet Rosie O'Grady 103

The dames of France are fond and free...(The Girl I Left Behind Me) 20

The harp that once through Tara's halls 22

Then drill, ye tarriers, drill 52

The minstrel boy to the war 43

The pale moon was rising above the green mountains...(The Rose of Tralee) 36

There they stand, hand in hand . . . (The Irish Wedding Song) 12

There's a dear little plant that grows in our isle...(The Green Little Shamrock) 54

There's a pretty spot in Ireland...(Where the River Shannon Flows) 62

There's a spot in me heart which no colleen may own...(Mother Machree) 98

There's a tear in your eye...(When Irish Eyes Are Smiling) 119

'Tis the last rose of summer 38

Too-ra-loo-ra-loo-ral, too-ra-loo-ra-li...(That's an Irish Lullaby) 106

Up to mighty London came an Irishman one day

    (It's a Long, Long Way to Tipperary) 70

When Irish eyes are smiling 119

Where dear old Shannon's flowing...(Where the River Shannon Flows) 62

Who is the man who will spend...(Harrigan) 79

Who threw the overalls in Mistress Murphy's chowder? 116

You can tell by the touch of the brogue...(You Can Tell That I'm Irish) 112

Young Rory O'More courted Kathleen Bawn...(Rory O'More) 34

The Irish Wedding Song
(The Wedding Song)

Words and Music by
IAN BETTERIDGE

God bless this coup - le____ who mar - ry to - day.
God bless this fam - 'ly____ who start - ed to - day.
God bless this coup - le____ who mar - ry to - day.

Chorus

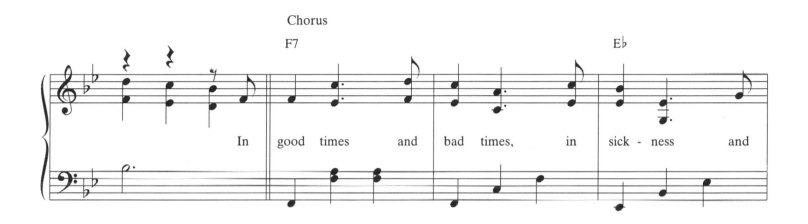

In good times and bad times, in sick - ness and

health,____ may they know that rich - es are not need - ed for

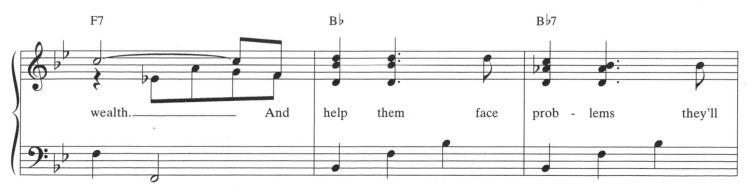

wealth.____ And help them face prob - lems they'll

ATF118

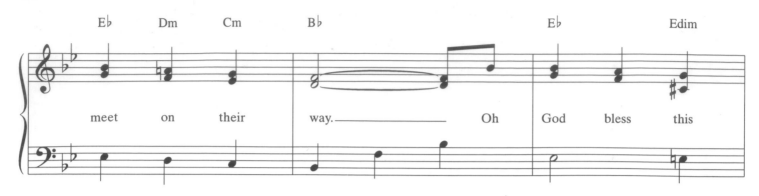

meet on their way._____ Oh God bless this

coup - le_____ who mar - ry to - day.

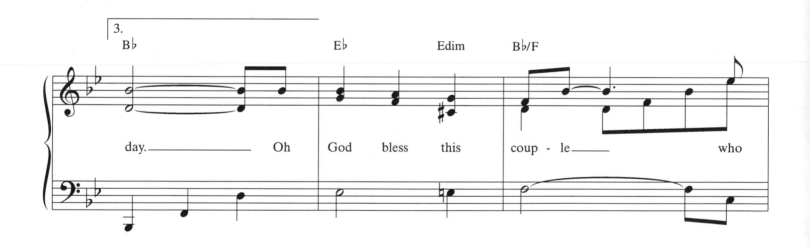

day._____ Oh God bless this coup - le_____ who

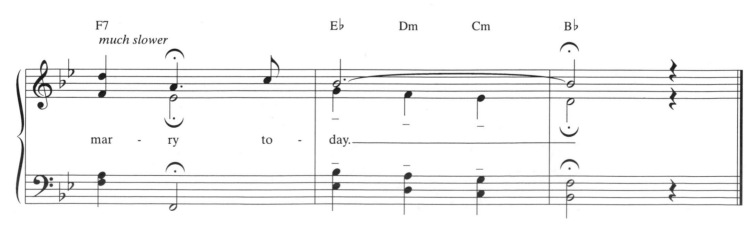

much slower

mar - ry to - day._____

The Songs of Old Ireland

Ireland

Believe Me
If All Those Endearing Young Charms

Words by
THOMAS MOORE
Music: TRADITIONAL

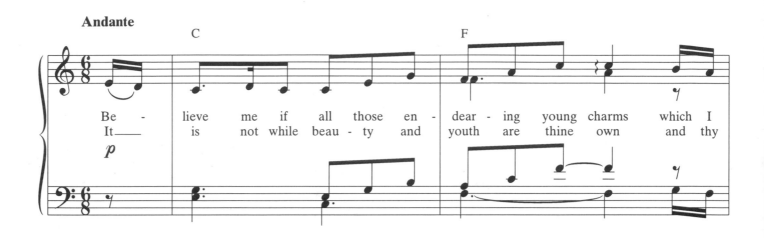

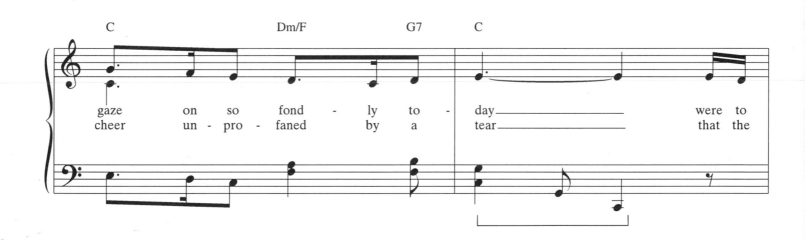

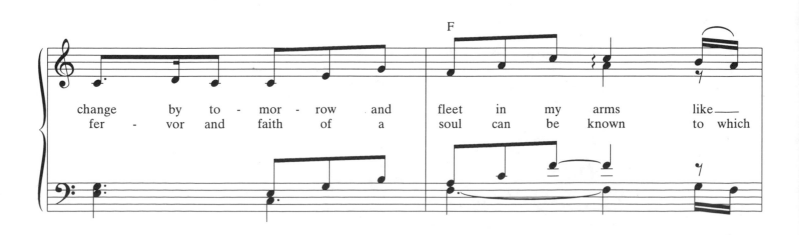

The Foggy Dew

Words by
ALFRED PERCIVAL GRAVES
Music: TRADITIONAL

Oh! a wan cloud was drawn o'er the dim weep-ing dawn, as to
But the sud-den sun kiss'd the cold cruel mist in-to

Shan-non's side I re-turned at last; and the
danc-ing show'rs of dia-mond dew; and the

heart in my breast, for the girl I love best, was
dark flow-ing stream laughed back to his beam, and the

Copyright © 1995 by Carl Fischer, Inc.

The Girl I Left Behind Me

TRADITIONAL

2. For she's as fair as Shannon's side,
   And purer than its water,
   But she refused to be my bride
   Though many a year I sought her;
   Yet, since to France I sailed away
   Her letters oft' remind me
   That I promised never to gainsay
   The girl I left behind me.

3. She says, "My own dear love, come home,
   My friends are rich and many,
   Or else abroad with you I'll roam,
   A soldier stout as any;
   If you'll not come, nor let me go,
   I'll think you have resigned me,"
   My heart nigh broke when I answered, "No,"
   To the girl I left behind me.

4. For never shall my true love brave
   A life of war and toiling,
   And never as a skulking slave
   I'll tread my native soil on;
   But were it free or to be freed,
   The battles close would find me,
   To Ireland bound, nor message need
   From the girl I left behind me.

The Harp That Once Through Tara's Halls

Words by
THOMAS MOORE
Music:
"GRAMACHREE"

Moderately fast

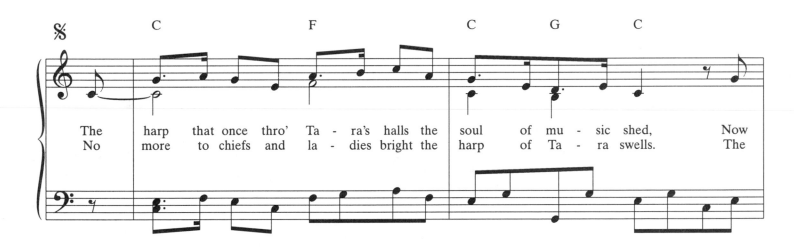

The harp that once thro' Ta - ra's halls the soul of mu - sic shed, Now
No more to chiefs and la - dies bright the harp of Ta - ra swells. The

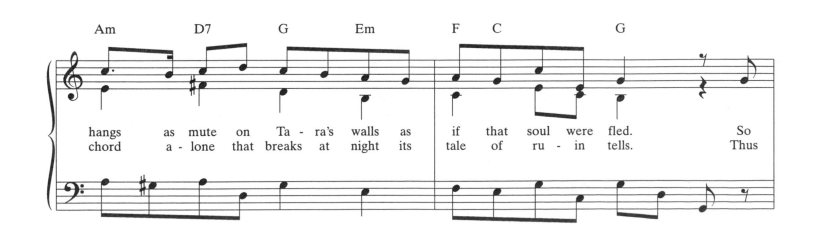

hangs as mute on Ta - ra's walls as if that soul were fled. So
chord a - lone that breaks at night its tale of ru - in tells. Thus

ATF118

The Irish Emigrant

Words by:
LADY DUFFERIN
Music by
G. BARKER

The Kerry Dance

Words and Music by
J. L. MOLLOY

2. Was there ever a sweeter colleen
   In the dance than Eily More?
   Or a prouder lad than Thady
   As he boldly took the floor!
   "Lads and lasses to your places,
   Up the middle an' down again,"
   Ah! the merry-hearted laughter
   Ringing through the happy glen!
   Oh, to think of it etc.

3. Loving voices of old companions,
   Stealing out of the past once more!
   And the sound of the dear old music
   Soft and sweet as in days of yore.
   When the boys began to gather
   In the glen of a summer night,
   And the Kerry piper's tuning
   Made us long with wild delight.
   Oh, to think of it etc.

Molly Bawn

Word and Music by
SAMUEL LOVER

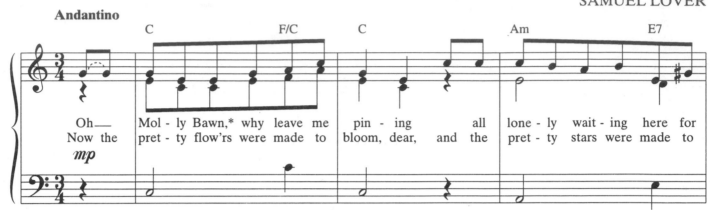

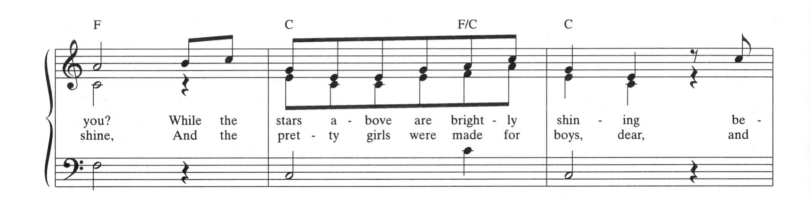

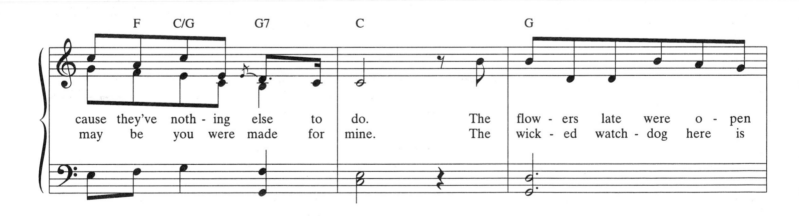

*Bawn means "fair" in Gaelic.

Molly Malone
(Cockles and Mussels)

TRADITIONAL

Andante (somewhat freely)

1. In Dub - lin's fair cit - y, where the girls are so
2. She was a fish - mong - er, but sure 'twas no
3. She died of a fe - ver*, and no one could

pret - ty, I first set my eyes on sweet
won - der, for so were her fa - ther and
save her, and that was the end of sweet

Mol - ly Ma - lone as she wheel'd her wheel -
moth - er be - fore. And they each wheel'd their
Mol - ly Ma - lone. But her ghost wheels her

bar - row
bar - row } thro' streets broad and nar - row cry - ing,
bar - row

*pronounced "fay-ver"

The Pretty Girl Milking Her Cow
(Colleen Dhas Cruthen Na Moe)

Words from the original Irish by
ALEXANDER LEE
Music: TRADITIONAL

Andantino (slowly, in 2; each ♩. = 1 beat)

It__ was on a fine sum - mer's morn - ing, the__ birds sweet - ly tuned on each bough,__ and__ as I walked out for my plea - sure, I saw a maid milk - ing her cow.__ Her voice so en - chant - ing mel - lo - dious left me quite__ un - a - ble to

Copyright © 1995 by Carl Fischer, Inc.

2. Then to her I made my advances:
   "Good morrow, most beautiful maid!
   Your beauty my heart so entrances,"
   "Pray sir, do not banter," she said.
   "I'm not such a rare precious jewel
   That I should enamor you so,
   I am but a poor little milk girl,"
   Says colleen dhas crutheen na moe.

3. The Indies afford no such jewel
   So bright and transparently clear,
   Ah, do not add flame to my fuel!
   Consent but to love me, my dear.
   Ah! had I the lamp of Aladdin,
   Or the wealth of the African shore,
   I would rather be poor in a cottage
   Wiith colleen dhas crutheen na moe.

Rory O'More

Words and Music by
SAMUEL LOVER

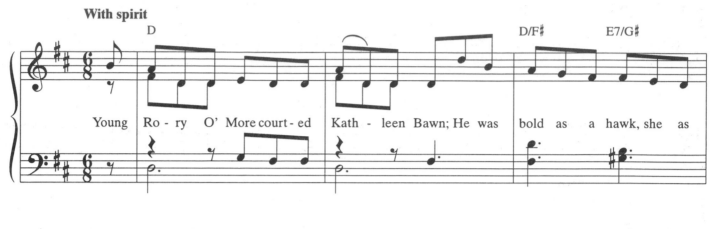

Young Ro-ry O' More court-ed Kath-leen Bawn; He was bold as a hawk, she as

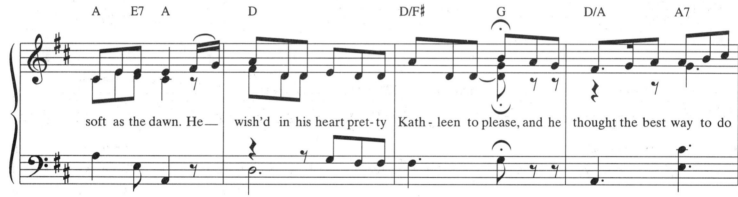

soft as the dawn. He— wish'd in his heart pret-ty Kath-leen to please, and he thought the best way to do

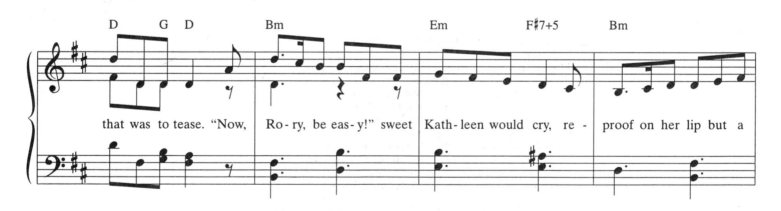

that was to tease. "Now, Ro-ry, be eas-y!" sweet Kath-leen would cry, re-proof on her lip but a

smile in her eye, "With your tricks I don't know in truth what I'm a-bout. Faith, you've

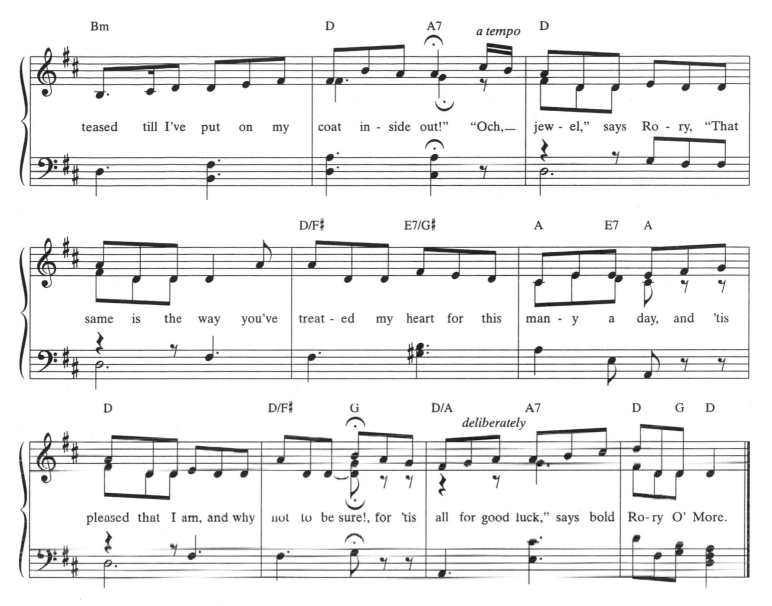

2. "Indeed then," says Kathleen, "don't think of the like,
For I half gave a promise to soothering Mike;
The ground that I walk on, he loves, I'll be bound,"
"Faith," says Rory, "I'd rather love you than the ground."
"Now, Rory, I'll cry if you don't let me go,
Sure I dreamed ev'ry night that I'm hating you so."
"Och," says Rory, "that same I'm delighted to hear,
For dreams always go by contraries, my dear;
So jewel, keep dreamin' that same till you die,
Bright mornin' will give dirty night the black lie,
And 'tis pleased that I am, and why not to be sure,
Since 'tis all for good luck," sings bold Rory O'More.

3. "Arrah, Kathleen, my darlin', you've teased me enough,
Since I've thrashed for your sake Dinny Grimes and Jim Duff,
And I've made myself, drinking your health, quite a beast,
So I think after that I may talk to the priest."
Then Rory, the rogue, stole his arm round her neck,
So soft and so white, without freckle or speck,
And he looked in her eyes that were beaming with light,
And he kissed her sweet lips, don't you think he was right?
"Now, Rory, leave off, sir, you'll hug me no more,
That's eight times today that you've kissed me before!"
"Then here goes another," says he, "to make sure,
For there's luck in odd numbers," says Rory O'More.

The Rose of Tralee

Words by
F. MORDAUNT SPENCER
Music by
CHARLES W. GLOVER

Flowing, not too fast

The pale moon was ris - ing a - bove the green
The cool shades of eve - ning their man - tle were

moun - tain, The sun was de - clin - ing be - neath, the blue
spread - ing And Mar - y, all smil - ing, was list - 'ning to

sea, When I strayed with my love to the pure crys - tal
me. — The moon, thro' the val - ley, her pale rays was

foun - tain That stands in the beau - ti - ful vale of Tra -
shed - ding When I won the heart of the Rose of Tra -

'Tis the Last Rose of Summer

Words and Music by
THOMAS MOORE

flect back her_____ blush-es Or_____ give sigh_____ for_____ sigh.

2. I'll not leave thee, thou lone one
   To pine on the stem;
   Since the lovely are sleeping,
   Go sleep thou with them.
   Thus kindly I scatter
   Thy leaves o'er the bed
   Where thy mates of the garden
   Lie scentless and dead.

3. So soon may I follow,
   When friendships decay,
   And from love's shining circle
   The gems drop away!
   When true hearts lie withered,
   And fond ones are flown,
   Oh! who would inhabit
   This bleak world alone?

Kathleen Mavourneen*

Words by
ANNIE CRAWFORD
Music by
F. W. CROUCH

*Mavourneen is Gaelic for "my darling".

ATF118

The Minstrel Boy

Words and Music by
THOMAS MOORE

The Irish Come to America

Ireland

Donegal

Londonderry

Belfast

Athlone

Galway

Dublin

Tipperary

River Shannon

Tralee   Limerick

Waterford

Killarney

Kerry   County Cork

Blarney

The Wearing of the Green

Words by
DION BOUCICAULT
Music: TRADITIONAL

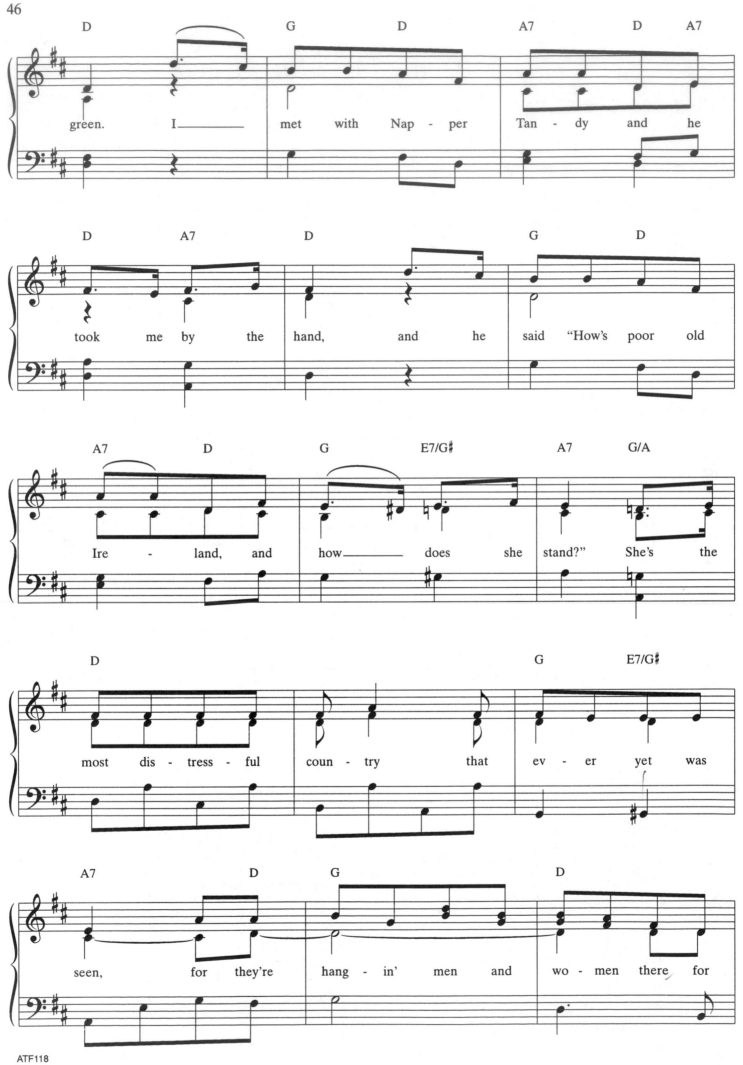

2. Then since the color we must wear
   Is England's cruel red,
   Sure Ireland's sons will ne'er forget
   The blood that they have shed.
   You may pull the shamrock from your hat
   And cast it on the sod,
   But 'twill take root and flourish there
   Tho' underfoot 'tis trod.
   When laws can stop the blades of grass
   From growin' as they grow,
   And when the leaves in summertime
   Their verdure dare not show,
   Then I will change the color, too,
   I wear in my caubeen,
   But till that day, please God, I'll stick
   To wearin' of the green!
   (repeat Chorus)

3. But if at last our color should
   Be torn from Ireland's heart,
   Her sons with shame and sorrow from
   The dear old isle will part.
   I've heard a whisper of a land
   That lies beyond the sea.
   Where rich and poor stand equal in
   The light of freedom's day.
   Ah, Erin, must we leave you driven
   By a tyrant's hand?
   Must we seek a mother's blessing
   From a strange and distant land?
   Where the cruel cross of England
   Shall never more be seen
   And where, please God, we'll live and die
   Still wearin' of the green!
   (repeat Chorus)

Come Back to Erin

Words and Music by
CLARIBEL

*Mavourneen is Gaelic for "my darling".

Danny Boy

Words by
FRED WEATHERLY
Music:
"LONDONDERRY AIR"

Copyright © 1995 by Carl Fischer, Inc.

Drill, Ye Tarriers,* Drill!

Words and Music by
THOMAS CASEY

*Tarrier - An Irish excavation worker.

2. The boss was a fine man all around,
   But he married a woman six feet around.
   She baked good bread and she baked it well,
   But she baked it hard as the hobs of hell!
   (Chorus)

3. The new foreman is Dan McCann,
   I'll tell you, sure, he's a blame mean man.
   Last week a premature blast went off
   And a mile in the air went big Jim Goff.
   (Chorus)

4. When payday next it came around
   Poor Jim's pay a dollar short be found.
   "What for?" says he. Came this reply:
   "You're docked for the time you were up in the sky!"
   (Chorus)

The Green Little Shamrock

(or, The Dear Little Shamrock)

TRADITIONAL

Copyright © 1995 by Carl Fischer, Inc.

I'll Take You Home Again, Kathleen

Words and Music by
THOMAS P. WESTENDORF

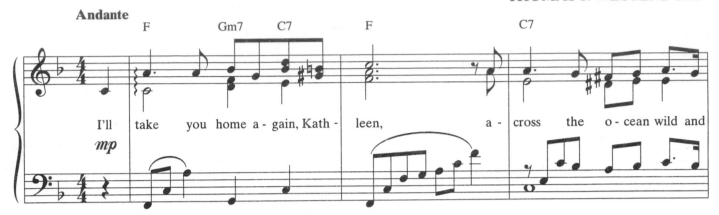

I'll take you home a - gain, Kath - leen, a - cross the o - cean wild and

wide to where your heart has ev - er been since

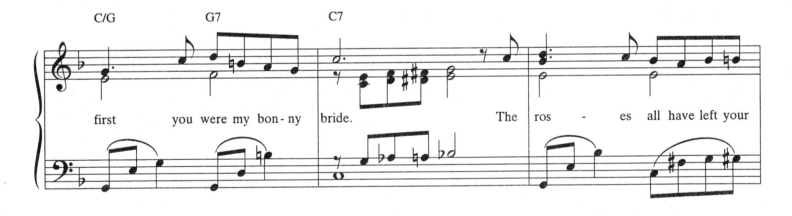

first you were my bon - ny bride. The ros - es all have left your

cheek; I've watched them fade a - way and die. Your

Copyright © 1995 by Carl Fischer, Inc.

2. I know you love me, Kathleen dear,
   Your heart was ever fond and true.
   I always feel when you are near
   That life holds nothing, dear, but you.
   The smiles that once you gave to me,
   I scarcely ever see them now,
   Tho' many many times I see
   A dark'ning shadow on your brow.
   (Repeat Chorus)

3. To that dear home beyond the sea
   My Kathleen shall again return.
   And when thy old friends welcome thee,
   Thy loving heart will cease to yearn.
   Where laughs the little silver stream
   Beside your mother's humble cot,
   And brightest rays of sunshine gleam,
   There all your grief will be forgot.
   (Repeat Chorus)

Killarney

Words by
EDMUND FALCONER
Music by
M.W. BALFE

2. Innisfallen's ruined shrine
   May suggest a passing sigh;
   But man's faith can ne'er decline
   Such God's wonders floating by.
   Castle Lough and Glena Bay:
   Mountains Tore and Eagles' Nest,
   Still at Mucross you must pray,
   Tho' the monks are now at rest;
   Angels wonder not that man
   There would fain prolong life's span,
   Beauty's home, Killarney,
   Ever fair, Killarney.

3. No place else can charm the eye
   With such bright and varied tints;
   Ev'ry rock that you pass by,
   Verdure broiders or besprints;
   Virgin there the green grass grows,
   Ev'ry morning springs natal day,
   Bright-hued berries daff the snows,
   Smiling winter's frown away.
   Angels often pausing there
   Doubt if Eden were more fair,
   Beauty's home, Killarney,
   Ever fair, Killarney.

4. Music there for Echo dwells,
   Makes each sound a harmony;
   Many-voiced the chorus swells
   Till it faints in ecstasy.
   With the charmful tints below,
   Seems the heav'n above to vie:
   All rich colors that we know
   Tinge the cloud-wreath in that sky.
   Wings of angels so might shine,
   Glancing back soft light divine,
   Beauty's home, Killarney,
   Ever fair, Killarney.

Paddy Works on the Railway

TRADITIONAL

Vigorously

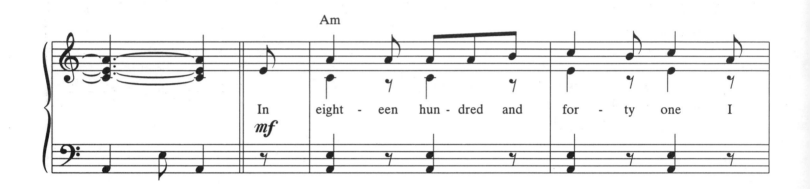

In eight - een hun - dred and for - ty one I

put my cor - du - roy brit - ches on, I put my cor - du - roy

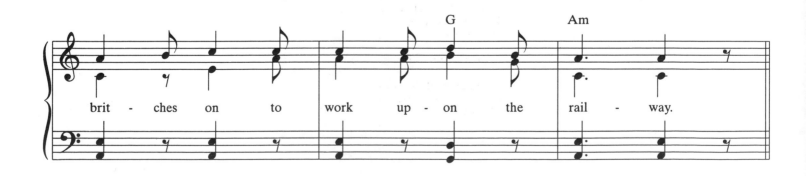

brit - ches on to work up - on the rail - way.

Chorus

Am   C

f Fil - le - me - oo - re - me - re - ay,   Fil - le - me - oo - re - le - re - ay,

Am   G   Am

Fil - le - me - oo - re - i - re - ay, to work up - on the rail - way.

2. In eighteen hundred and forty two
Looking around for something to do,
Looking around for something to do,
A - workin' on the railway.
(Chorus)

3. Well, it's "Pat, do this," and "Pat, do that!"
Without a stocking or cravat,
And nothing but an old straw hat
While working on the railway.
(Chorus)

4. In eighteen hundred forty three
'Twas then I met sweet Biddy McGee,
An elegant wife she's been to me
While working on the railway.
(Chorus)

5. In eighteen hundred and forty seven
Sweet Biddy McGee she went to heaven.
If she left one child she left eleven
To work upon the railway.
(Chorus)

6. In eighteen hundred and forty eight
I learned to drink me whiskey straight,
It's an elegant drink that can't be bate
For working on the railway.
(Chorus)

Where the River Shannon Flows

Words and Music by
JAMES I. RUSSELL

That Tumble-down Shack in Athlone

Words by
RICHARD W. PASCOE
Music by
MONTE CARLO and ALMA M. SANDERS

Andante moderato (moving along, but not rushed)

Verse - freely

I'm a long way from home, and my thoughts ev - er roam to ould
There are eyes that are sad as they watch for a lad in the

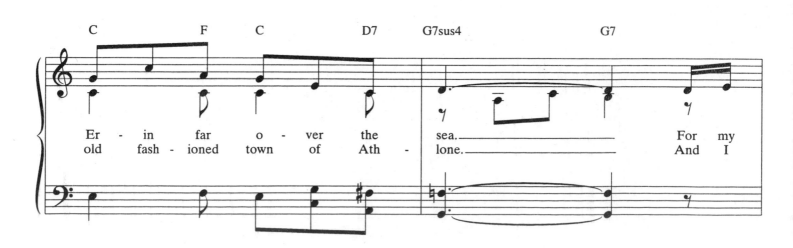

Er - in far o - ver the sea. For my
old fash - ioned town of Ath - lone. And I

The Irish
on Stage

Ireland

Donegal
Londonderry
Belfast

Galway
Athlone
Dublin

Tipperary

River Shannon
Tralee   Limerick
Waterford
Killarney
Kerry   County Cork
Blarney

Ireland Must Be Heaven
(For My Mother Came from There)

Words and Music by
JOSEPH McCARTHY, HOWARD JOHNSON
and FRED FISHER

Moderately and somewhat freely throughout

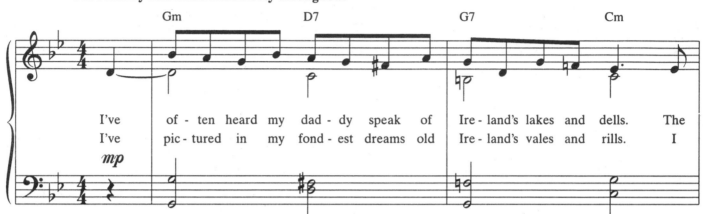

I've of-ten heard my dad-dy speak of Ire-land's lakes and dells. The
I've pic-tured in my fond-est dreams old Ire-land's vales and rills. I

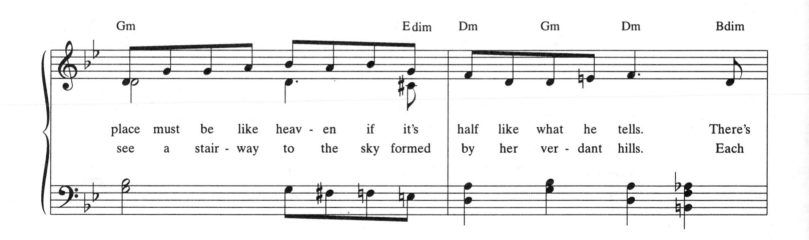

place must be like heav-en if it's half like what he tells. There's
see a stair-way to the sky formed by her ver-dant hills. Each

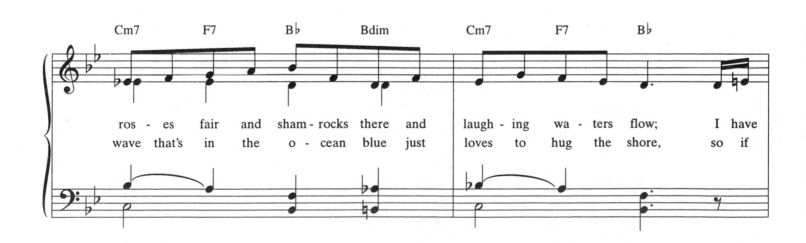

ros-es fair and sham-rocks there and laugh-ing wa-ters flow; I have
wave that's in the o-cean blue just loves to hug the shore, so if

nev - er seen that isle of green, but there's one thing sure I know:
Ire - land is - n't heav - en, then sure it must be right next door:

Chorus

Ire - land must be heav - en, for an an - gel came from there; I

nev - er knew a liv - ing soul one half as sweet or fair. For her

eyes are like the star - light, and the white clouds match her hair. Sure,

Ire - land must be heav - en, for my moth - er came from there!

It's a Long, Long Way to Tipperary

Words and Music by
JACK JUDGE and HARRY WILLIAMS

Has Anybody Here Seen Kelly?

Words and Music by
C.W. MURPHY and WILL LETTERS
American version by
WILLIAM J. McKENNA

Kel - ly lost his little girl up - on the Great White Way. She
Kel - ly's fav - 'rite song, so Mar - y said, "I'll find him there." She

walked up - town from Her - ald Square to For - ty Sec - ond street. The
climbed up - on the grand - stand in hopes her Mike she'd see; The Five

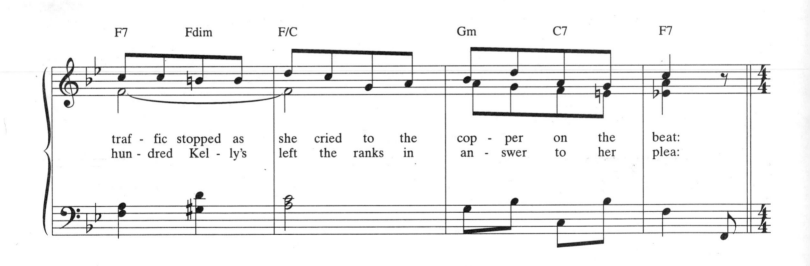

traf - fic stopped as she cried to the cop - per on the beat:
hun - dred Kel - ly's left the ranks in an - swer to her plea:

Chorus **Marcato** (♪ = ♪)

Has an - y - bod - y here seen Kel - ly?_____ K. E.

mf

I've Got Rings on My Fingers

(or, Mumbo Jumbo Jijjiboo J. O'Shea)

Words by
WESTON and BARNES
Music by
MAURICE SCOTT

Moderately

Verse

1. Jim O' Shea was cast a - way up - on an In - dian isle. The na - tives there they liked his hair, they liked his I - rish smile, so made him chief pan - jan - drum, the na - bob of them all. They

Additional Verses

2. O'er the sea went Rose McGee to see her nabob grand,
   He sat within his palanquin, and when she kissed his hand
   He led her to his harem where he had wives galore.
   She started shedding a tear;
   Said he, "Now have no fear!
   I'm keeping those wives here
   Just for ornament, my dear:
   (repeat Chorus)

3. Emerald green he robed his queen to share with him his throne;
   'Mid eastern charms and waving palms they'd shamrocks Irish grown.
   Sent all the way from Dublin to nabob J. O'Shea,
   But in his palace so fine,
   Should Rose for Ireland pine,
   With smiles her face will shine,
   When he murmurs, "Sweetheart mine:
   (repeat Chorus to Final ending)

Harrigan

Words and Music by
GEORGE M. COHAN

Moderately, with a lilt

Verse

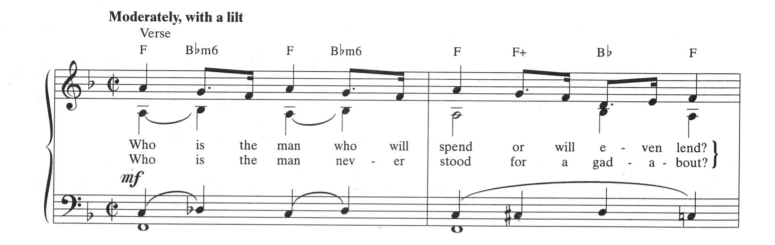

Who is the man who will spend or will e - ven lend?
Who is the man nev - er stood for a gad - a - bout?

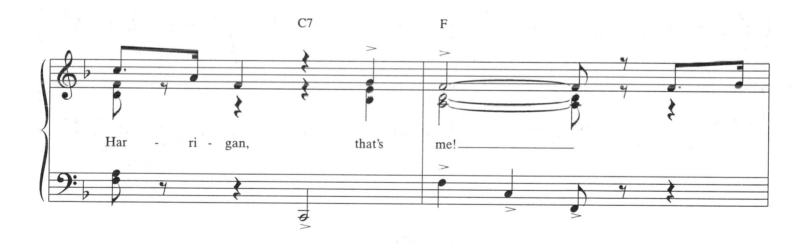

Har - ri - gan, that's me!

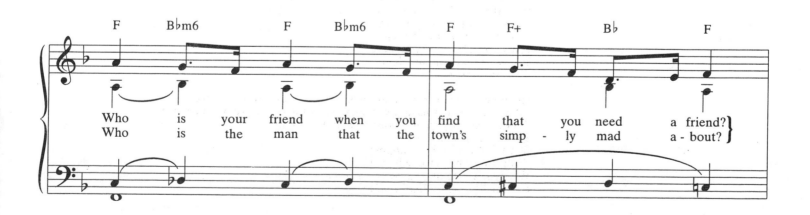

Who is your friend when you find that you need a friend?
Who is the friend man that when you the town's simp - ly mad a - bout?

Macushla

Words by
JOSEPHINE V. ROWE
Music by
DERMOT MacMURROUGH

Copyright © 1995 by Carl Fischer, Inc.

A Little Bit of Heaven
(Shure They Call It Ireland)

Words by
J. KEIRN BRENNAN
Music by
ERNEST R. BALL

Moderately and somewhat freely throughout

Copyright © 1995 by Carl Fischer, Inc.

here's the way me dear old moth - er told the tale to me:____
lit - tle bit of heav - en and I love it more and more:____

Chorus

Shure a lit - tle bit of heav - en fell from out the sky one day and

nes - tled on the o - cean in a spot so far a - way. And

when the an - gels found it, shure, it looked so sweet and fair; They

Little Annie Rooney

Words and Music by
MICHAEL NOLAN

Waltz

A
We've

Verse

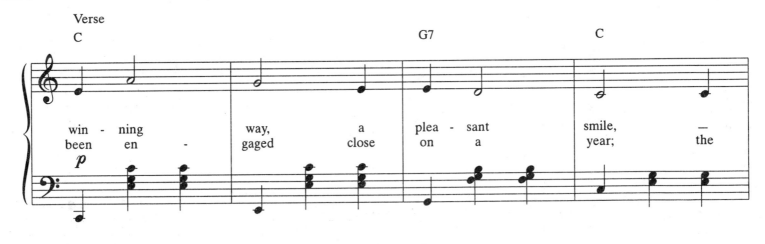

C   G7   C

win - ning   way,   a   plea - sant   smile,   —
been en -   gaged   a   close   on   a   year;   the

F   C/E   C♯dim   G7

dressed   so   neat   but   quite   in   style,   —
hap - py   time   is   draw - ing   near.   I'll

ATF118

lit - tle An - nie Roo - ney.
lit - le An - nie Roo - ney.

Chorus
C
She's my sweet - heart,

F   C
I'm her beau;———————

F   C
She's my An - nie,———————

Am   D7   G7
I'm her Joe.———————

ATF118

Mary's a Grand Old Name

Words and Music by
GEORGE M. COHAN

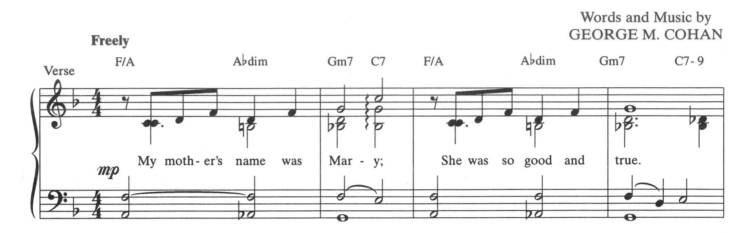

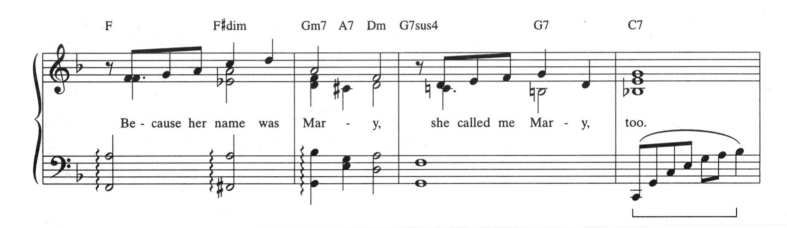

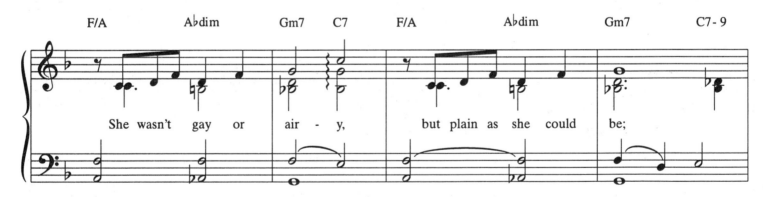

*originally "square"

ATF118

McNamara's Band

Words by
JOHN J. STAMFORD
Music by
SHAMUS O'CONNOR

Oh, me name is Mc Nam - a - ra, I'm the
now we are re - hear - sin' for a

lead - er of the band._____ Al - though we're few in
ver - y swell af - fair,_____ the an - nual cel - e

Mother Machree*

Words by
RIDA JOHNSON YOUNG
Music by
CHAUNCEY OLCOTT and ERNEST R. BALL

Allegretto, with expression

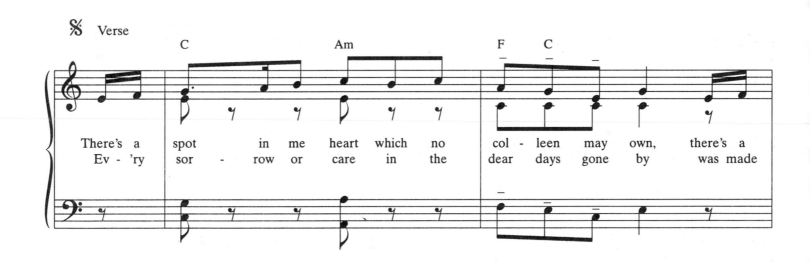

Verse

There's a spot in me heart which no col-leen may own, there's a
Ev - 'ry sor - row or care in the dear days gone by was made

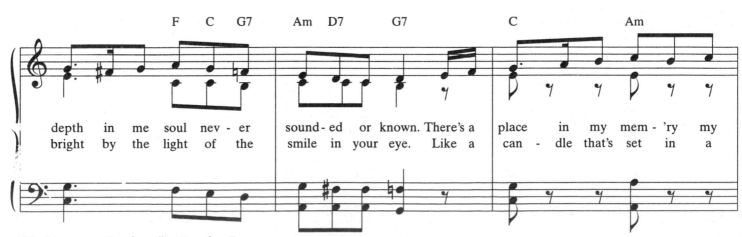

depth in me soul nev - er sound - ed or known. There's a place in my mem - 'ry my
bright by the light of the smile in your eye. Like a can - dle that's set in a

*Machree means "my heart" or "my dear."

My Wild Irish Rose

Words and Music by
CHAUNCEY OLCOTT

Sweet Rosie O'Grady

Words and Music by
MAUD NUGENT

Copyright © 1995 by Carl Fischer, Inc.

Moderate waltz

Sweet Ro - sie O' Gra - dy, my dear lit - tle rose; She's my stead - y la - dy, most ev - 'ry - one knows. And when we are mar -

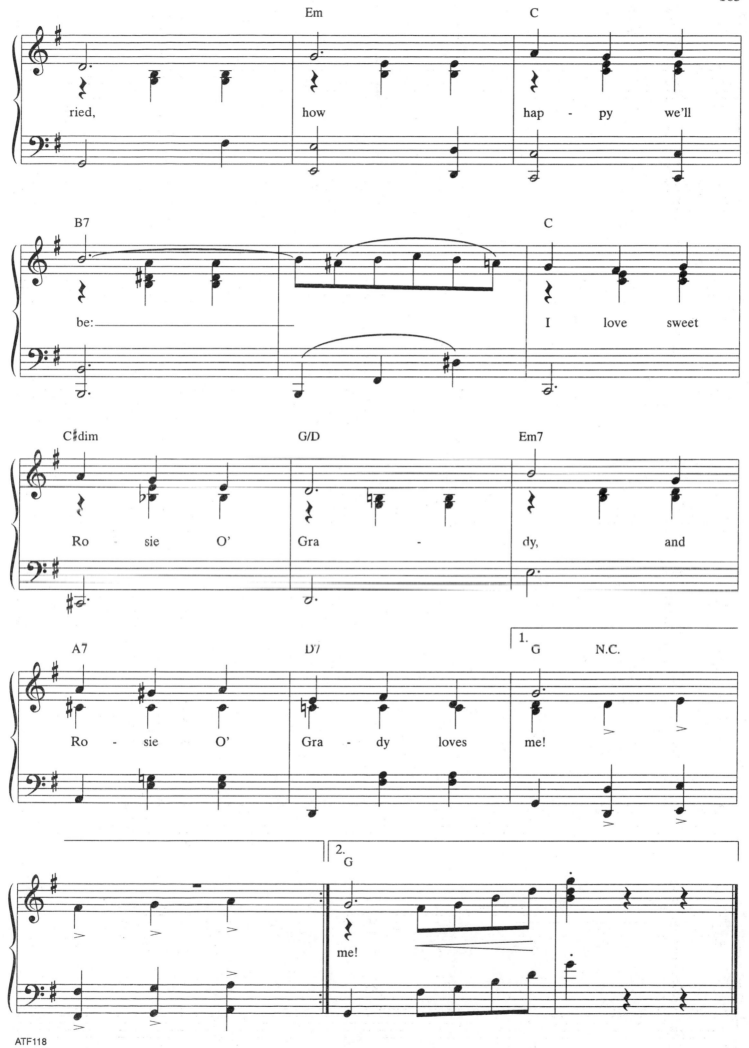

Too-ra-loo-ra-loo-ral
(That's an Irish Lullaby)

Words and Music by
J.R. SHANNON

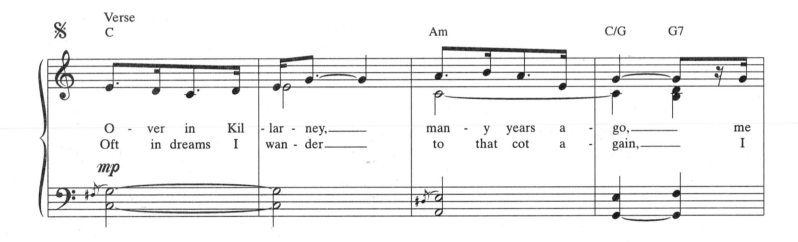

O - ver in Kil - lar - ney,_____ man - y years a - go,_____ me
Oft in dreams I wan - der_____ to that cot a - gain,_____ I

mith - er sang a song to me in tones so sweet and
feel her arms a - hug - gin' me as when she held me

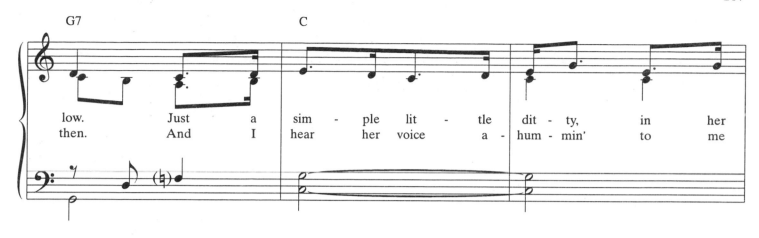

G7   C

low.   Just   a   sim - ple lit - tle   dit - ty,   in   her
then.   And   I   hear   her   voice   a - hum - min'   to   me

Am   C   F

good   ould   I - rish   way,   and   I'd   give   the   world   if
as   in   days   of   yore,   when   she   used   to   rock   me

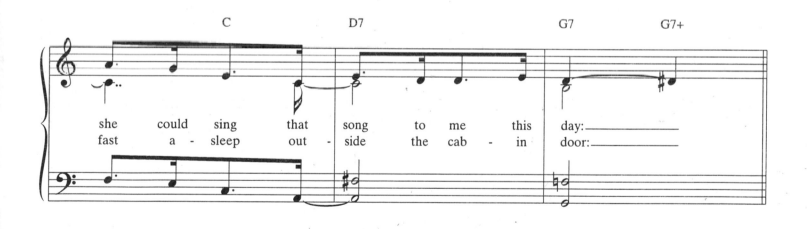

C   D7   G7   G7+

she   could   sing   that   song   to   me   this   day:_____
fast   a - sleep   out - side   the   cab - in   door:_____

Chorus

C   C7   F

Too - ra - loo - ra - loo - ral,_____   too - ra - loo - ra -

p

Peg O' My Heart

Words by
ALFRED BRYAN
Music by
FRED FISCHER

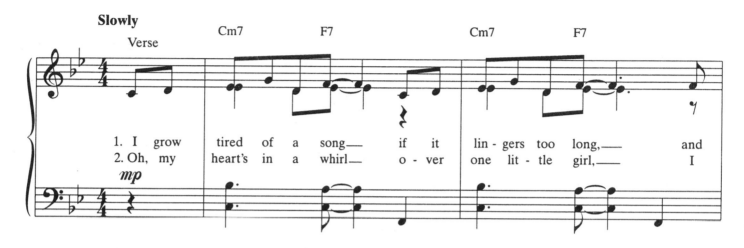

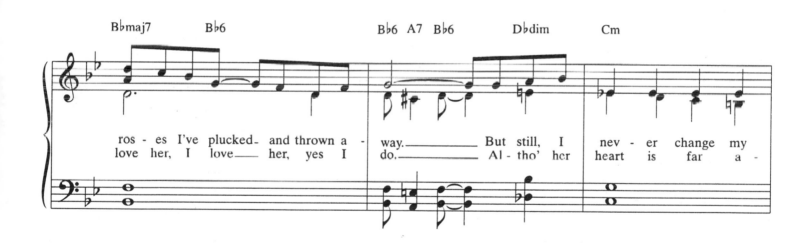

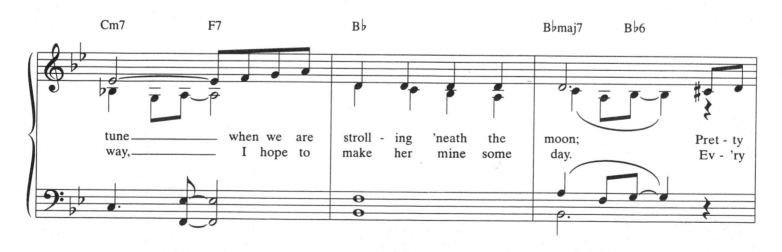

You Can Tell That I'm Irish

Words and Music by
GEORGE M. COHAN

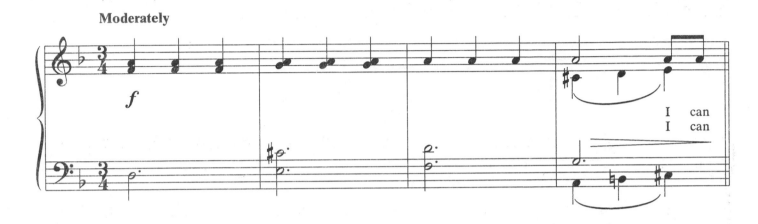

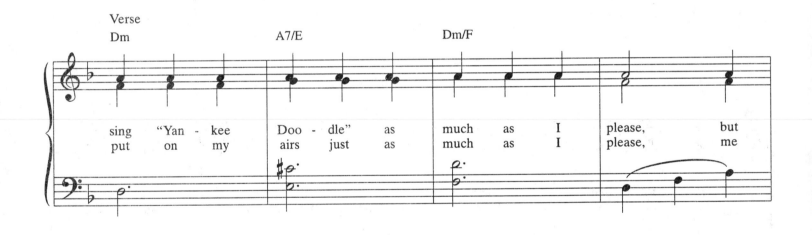

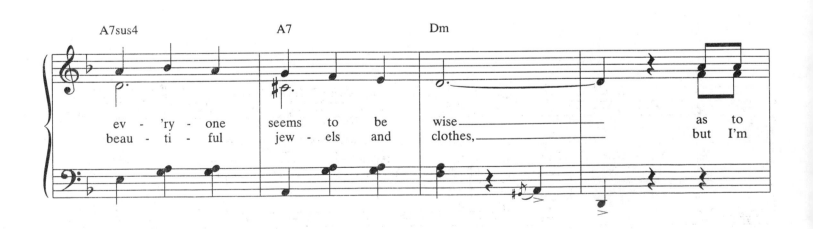

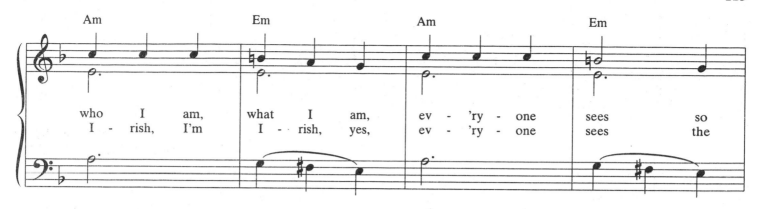

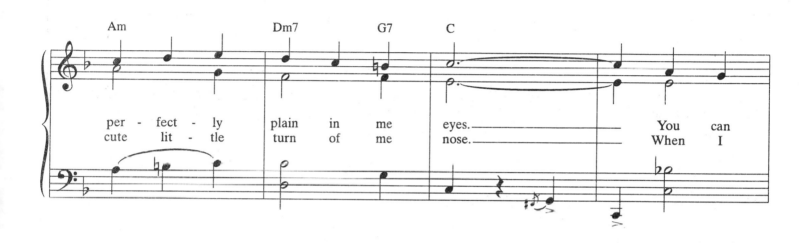

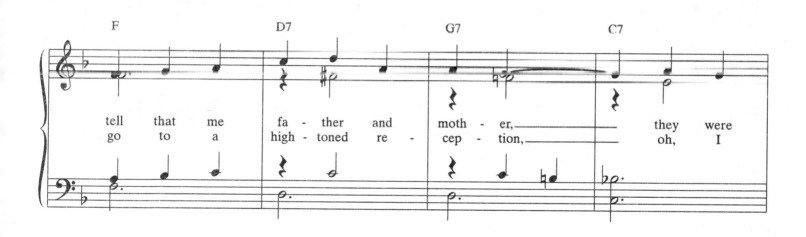

*Maggie Cline was an Irish-American vaudevillian of the turn
of the century whose lusty rendition of "Throw 'Em Down, McCloskey"
made her a star.

Who Threw The Overalls in Mistress Murphy's Chowder?

Words and Music by
GEORGE L. GEIFER

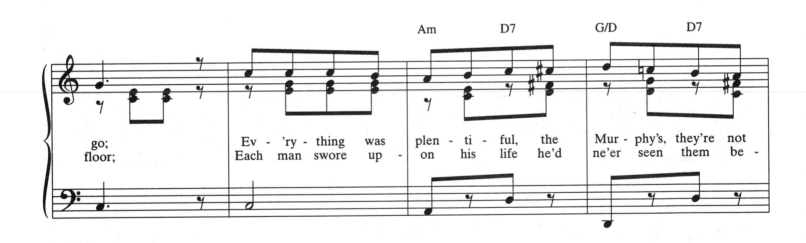

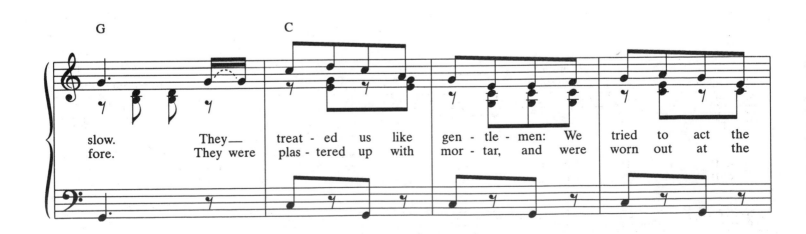

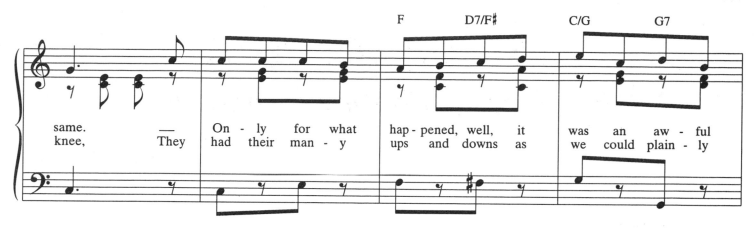

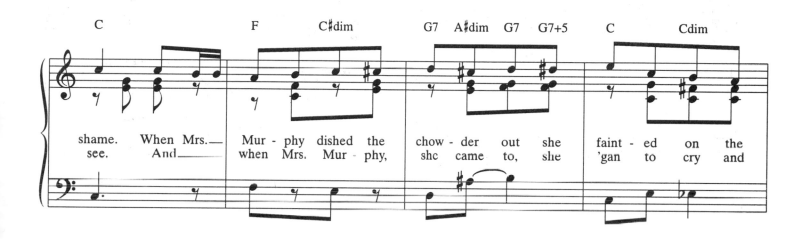

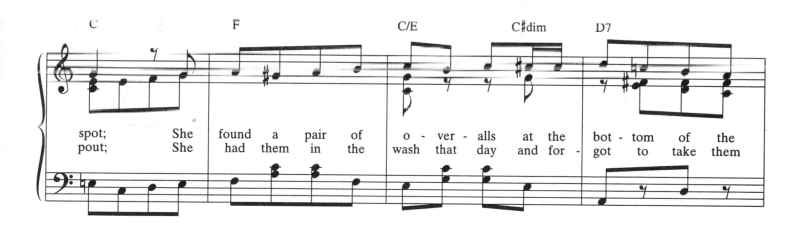

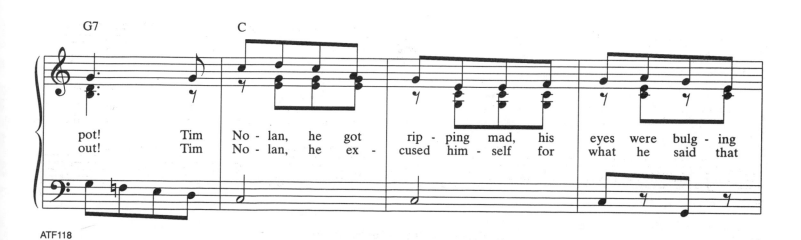

ATF118

When Irish Eyes Are Smiling

Words by
CHAUNCEY OLCOTT and GEO. GRAFF, Jr.
Music by
ERNEST R. BALL

Copyright © 1995 by Carl Fischer, Inc.

Jigs, Reels and Hornpipes

Ireland

Donegal

Londonderry

Belfast

Athlone

Galway

Dublin

Tipperary

River Shannon

Tralee

Limerick

Waterford

Killarney

Kerry

County Cork

Blarney

Devil's Dream

HORNPIPE

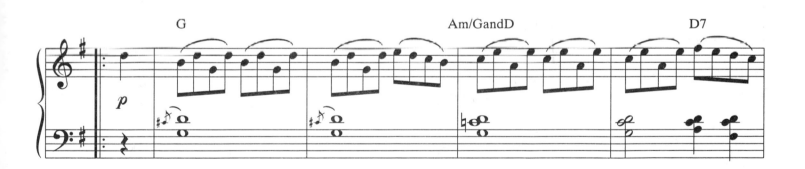

Copyright © 1995 by Carl Fischer, Inc.

Garryowen

JIG

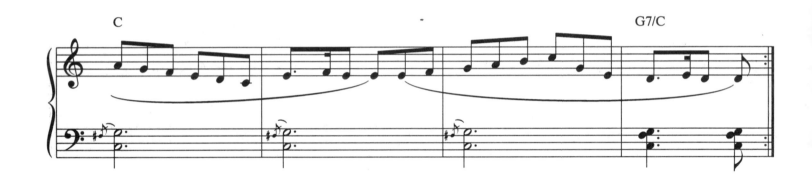

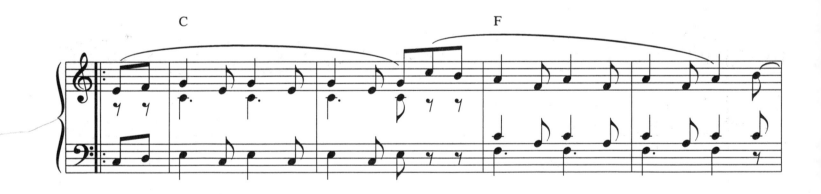

The Irish Washerwoman

TRADITIONAL JIG

Paddy Whack

JIG

St. Patrick's Day in the Morning

TRADITIONAL JIG

Stack O' Barley

REEL